MATSYA AVATAR

EXHAUSTED, BRAHMA STRETCHED OUT AND YAWNED. HIS DAY'S WORK WAS OVER. THE END OF THE CURRENT KALPA WAS IMMINENT. AS HIS EYE-LIDS DROOPED WITH SLEEP, WITHOUT HIS KNOWLEDGE THE VEDAS SLIPPED OUT OF HIS MOUTH.

THE ASURA, HAYAGRIVA, WAS ALERT.

THIS IS MY CHANCE! I MUST NOW CONCENTRATE WITH ALL MY MIND AND THE VEDAS FALLING OUT OF THE CREA-TOR'S MOUTH WILL ENTER MINE.

BUT VISHNU, THE PRESERVER, CAUGHT HAYAGRIVA IN THE ACT.

THE ASURA IS ABSORBING THE VEDAS. THEY WILL BE LOST TO THE NEXT KALPA. I MUST RETRIEVE THEM. THERE ARE BUT A FEW DAYS LEFT FOR PRALAYA.*

AS HE WONDERED WHAT TO DO, HE SAW THE ROYAL SAGE, SATYAVRATA, A STAUNCH DEVOTEE, OFFERING WATER TO THE MANES.

I WILL TAKE THE FORM OF A FISH AND RETRIEVE THE VEDAS WHILE DOING A GOOD TURN TO MY DEV-OTEE. HE SHALL LIVE THROUGH PRALAYA TO BECOME THE MANU OF THE SEVENTH MAN-VANTARA OF THE NEXT KALPA.

AS SATYAVRATA, SCOOPED UP THE NEXT HANDFUL OF WATER —

WHAT'S THIS? A WEE FISH. POOR CREATURE. HOW FRIGHTENED IT MUST BE! I'LL DROP IT BACK INTO THE RIVER.

HE WAS ABOUT TO DO SO WHEN —

O KIND KING, DO NOT THROW ME BACK INTO THE WATER. HELPLESS AS I AM, OTHER CREATURES OF THE RIVER WILL SOON EAT ME UP.

SATYAVRATA WAS MOVED.

DON'T FEAR, LITTLE ONE. I WILL CER-TAINLY PROTECT YOU.

HE PUT THE FISH INTO HIS KAMANDALU...

...AND TOOK IT TO HIS HERMITAGE.

THAT NIGHT, HOWEVER, THE FISH GREW AND GREW TILL IT FILLED THE WHOLE KAMANDALU.

IN THE MORNING WHEN SATYAVRATA WENT TO SEE IF IT WAS ALL RIGHT—

O KING, THIS KAMANDALU IS TOO SMALL. PLEASE FIND A MORE SPACIOUS VESSEL FOR ME.

REMOVING IT FROM THE KAMANDALU, SATYAVRATA PLACED IT IN A LARGE VESSEL OF WATER.

BUT WITHIN BARELY AN HOUR—

O KING, EVEN THIS VESSEL IS TOO SMALL. I HAVE SOUGHT YOUR PROTECTION. YOU MUST FIND THE LIVING SPACE FOR ME.

SATYAVRATA PUSHED THE VESSEL TO A LARGE POND NEAR THE HERMITAGE AND TIPPED THE FISH INTO IT.

BUT IN NO TIME, THE FISH GREW TILL IT FILLED THE WHOLE POND.

O KING, LEAD ME TO A LAKE—A DEEP, LARGE ONE. I WILL DIE IF I REMAIN HERE.

SATYAVRATA TOOK THE FISH TO A NUMBER OF LAKES, EACH LARGER THAN THE PREVIOUS ONE. BUT—

I NEED MORE WATER, O KING. YOU ARE BOUND TO PROVIDE IT.

EXASPERATED, SATYAVRATA DECIDED TO LEAD IT TO THE OCEAN. BUT WHEN THEY GOT THERE—

O VALIANT KING, DO NOT LEAVE ME HERE AND GO. THE GIGANTIC CREATURES OF THE SEA MAY EAT ME.

SATYAVRATA NOW BECAME SUSPICIOUS.

WHO ARE YOU? I HAVE NEITHER SEEN NOR HEARD OF A WONDERFUL CREATURE LIKE YOU. IN ONE DAY YOU HAVE GROWN BIG ENOUGH TO COVER THE LARGEST OF LAKES.

COULD YOU BE...?

YOU ARE! LORD NARAYANA*, FORGIVE ME!

AND SATYAVRATA PROSTRATED HIMSELF BEFORE THE FISH.

HAIL TO YOU, SUPREME ONE. I KNOW YOU ASSUME DIFFERENT FORMS AND COME TO EARTH FOR THE GOOD OF ALL BUT...

...WHY HAVE YOU COME IN THIS LOWLY FORM?

THE LORD LOOKED LOVINGLY AT HIS DEVOTEE.

SEVEN DAYS FROM NOW, ALL THE THREE WORLDS WILL BE SUBMERGED BY THE OCEAN WHICH WILL RISE FOR THE DISSOLUTION OF CREATION.

*ANOTHER NAME OF VISHNU.

AT THAT TIME A SPACIOUS BOAT SENT BY ME WILL APPROACH YOU.

MEANWHILE, YOU MUST COLLECT ALL THE HERBS AND SEEDS AND ANIMALS YOU WANT FOR THE NEXT KALPA. THEN, ALONG WITH THE SAPTA RISHIS,* GET INTO THE BOAT AND AWAIT ME. DON'T FORGET TO BRING VASU-KI, KING OF THE SER-PENTS, WITH YOU.

AND THE FISH SET OFF ON ITS OTHER MISSION.

WHEN HAYAGRIVA SAW THE GIGANTIC FISH APPROACH, HE WAS FILLED WITH TERROR.

BUT I MUST NOT OPEN MY MOUTH LEST I LOSE THE VEDAS.

THAT WAS EASIER SAID THAN DONE. THE FISH SOON PUT AN END TO HIM AND —

THERE! THE VEDAS ARE SAFE. I WILL RESTORE THEM TO BRAHMA AS HE WAKES UP FROM HIS SLUMBER IMMEDIATELY BEFORE THE NEXT KALPA.

* SEVEN SAGES

SEVEN DAYS LATER, HUGE CLOUDS GATHERED OVER THE OCEAN. THE RAIN POURED DOWN IN TORRENTS. THE OCEAN BEGAN RISING AND HUGE TIDAL WAVES BEGAN SWALLOWING THE EARTH.

MEDITATE ON THE LORD. HE HAS PROMISED US DELIVERANCE.

AS ADVISED BY THE FISH, SATYAVRATA AND THE SAPTA RISHIS WAITED ON THE SHORES. SUDDENLY —

AH! THERE COMES THE BOAT AS THE LORD HAD PROMISED. BE PREPARED TO GO ON BOARD.

AS SOON AS THE VESSEL TOUCHED THE SHORES, SATYAVRATA, ALONG WITH THE SAPTA RISHIS AND THE SELECT LIVING CREATURES, BOARDED IT.

AS THEIR BOAT WAS TOSSED ABOUT BY THE TURBULENT OCEAN, THEY SUDDENLY SAW THE FISH APPROACH THEM. IT HAD A HORN NOW AND WAS GOLDEN IN COLOUR. IT LIT UP THE DARKENING SKIES, REASSURING THE INMATES OF THE BOAT.

FASTEN THE VESSEL TO MY HORN, USING VASUKI AS A ROPE. DO NOT FEAR. NOT ONE OF YOU SHALL COME TO ANY HARM.

WHILE THEY SAILED ON THAT VAST EXPANSE OF WATER, THROUGHOUT THAT NIGHT*OF BRAHMA, VISHNU TAUGHT SATYAVRATA AND THE SAPTA RISHIS THE HIGHEST FORM OF TRUTH WHICH HAS COME DOWN TO US AS A COLLECTION OF PURANIC LORE, CALLED THE MATSYA PURANA. THUS DID VISHNU SAVE TRUE DEVOTEES FROM DISSOLUTION SO THAT THEY MIGHT CARRY DIVINE KNOWLEDGE TO THE NEXT KALPA.

* EQUIVALENT TO A DAY OF BRAHMA.

KURMA AVATAR

IT WAS THE SIXTH MANVANTARA OF THE PRESENT KALPA. INDRA, KING OF THE DEVAS, AND HIS SUBJECTS WERE IN TROUBLE. CONSULTATIONS AMONG THEMSELVES DID NOT PROVIDE ANY SOLUTION. SO THEY DECIDED TO GO TO BRAHMA THE CREATOR, WHO LIVED ON MOUNT MERU.

AT MOUNT MERU —

SIRE, WE HAVE COME TO YOU FOR HELP. THE CURSE OF DURVASA HAS TURNED US INTO A WEAK AND LACK-LUSTRE LOT. WE ARE HELPLESS AGAINST OUR FOES, THE ASURAS.

WE BECOME LISTLESS ON THE BATTLEFIELD AND OUR FORCES FALL DEAD IN LARGE NUM-BERS, NEVER TO RISE AGAIN.

BRAHMA MEDITATED FOR A WHILE. THEN—

LET US TAKE REFUGE IN LORD VISHNU. HE ALWAYS HELPS THOSE WHO PLACE FAITH IN HIM. BESIDES, IT IS HE WHO PRESERVES THE ORDER OF THE UNIVERSE.

SO THEY WENT TO THE ABODE OF VISHNU, THE PRESERVER.

O OMNISCIENT ONE, YOU KNOW WHY WE, THE GUARDIANS OF THE WORLD, HAVE COME. WE SURRENDER OURSELVES TO YOU. SHOW US A WAY OUT OF OUR PLIGHT.

LORD VISHNU SPOKE IN HIS DEEP, RESONANT VOICE.

YOU WILL HAVE TO STRIVE HARD AND OBTAIN THE NECTAR OF IMMORTALITY. THAT IS THE ONLY WAY OUT FOR YOU.

HOW SHOULD WE OBTAIN THE NECTAR, O LORD?

YOU MUST CAST ALL KINDS OF PLANTS, HERBS, GRASSES AND CREEPERS INTO THE OCEAN OF MILK. THEN CHURN THE OCEAN USING MOUNT MANDARA AS A CHURN-DASHER AND VASUKI, KING OF THE SERPENTS, AS THE ROPE FOR TURNING IT.

BUT LORD, HOW ARE WE TO SHIFT MOUNT MANDARA?

MAKE PEACE WITH YOUR COUSINS AND ENEMIES, THE ASURAS AND USE THEM TO ACHIEVE YOUR END.

YOU MUST BE CAREFUL, HOW-EVER, NOT TO COVET ANY OF THE THINGS THAT COME OUT OF THE OCEAN AND NOT TO GIVE VENT TO ANGER EVEN IF THOSE THINGS ARE FORCIBLY TAKEN BY THE ASURAS.

B-B-BUT THE NECTAR? IF THEY SNATCH THE NECTAR?

I PROMISE YOU THAT YOUR AGGRESSIVE COUSINS WILL NOT ENJOY ANY PART OF THE NECTAR, FOR ALL THEIR TOIL.

BRAHMA RETURNED TO HIS OWN ABODE WHILE INDRA AND THE DEVAS SET OUT FOR THE COURT OF BALI, KING OF THE ASURAS.

WHEN BALI AND HIS ASURA FOLLOWING SAW THEIR ENEMIES APPROACH—

O KING, LET US CAPTURE THE ROGUES. THEY ARE UNARMED AND HELPLESS.

NO. WAIT. PERHAPS THE DEVAS COME WITH A PROPOSAL THAT MIGHT BE WORTH OUR WHILE.

BALI RECEIVED INDRA AND THE DEVAS WITH RESPECT AND GAVE THEM SEATS OF HONOUR. INDRA TOLD HIM WHY THEY HAD COME.

...AND SO, FOR THE BENEFIT OF ALL OF US, I REQUEST YOU TO FORGET OUR FEUD AND WORK WITH US IN THE VENTURE.

BALI, AS WELL AS HIS CHIEFS, FAVOURED THE PROPOSAL AND PEACE WAS DECLARED BETWEEN THE ASURAS AND THE DEVAS.

LET US NOT WASTE ANY TIME, INDRA. RALLY YOUR FORCES WHILE I RALLY MINE AND LET US BEGIN THE WORK IMMEDIATELY.

A LITTLE LATER, ALONG WITH THEIR HORDES, BALI AND INDRA BEGAN THE TASK OF UPROOTING MOUNT MANDARA...

...AND TAKING IT TO THE SEASHORE.

BUT WHEN THEY HAD BARELY COVERED HALF THE DISTANCE —

OO-OH! I CANNOT CARRY IT ANY FARTHER.

MY ARMS HAVE ALMOST FALLEN OUT OF THEIR SOCKETS.

WHY DID WE EVER AGREE TO SUCH AN INSANE PROPOSAL?

BEWARE!

ALAS! WHAT A FATE!

MOVE OUT OF THE WAY!

THE MIGHTY MOUNTAIN FELL, CRUSHING LARGE NUMBERS OF DEVAS AND ASURAS UNDER IT. INDRA WAS DESPERATE.

O LORD, WHAT ARE WE TO DO NOW? PLEASE COME TO OUR AID, OR WE SHALL PERISH.

MEANWHILE —

FASTER, GARUDA*! THE DEVAS ARE IN TROUBLE.

EVEN BEFORE INDRA APPEALED TO HIM, THE LORD HAD REACHED THE SPOT.

WITH A MERE GLANCE, HE REVIVED THE DEVAS.

THEN, PLACING MOUNT MANDARA ON GARUDA'S BACK, HE FLEW TO THE SEASHORE, FOLLOWED BY THE DEVAS AND THE ASURAS.

* VISHNU'S MOUNT.

AFTER THE MOUNTAIN WAS SAFELY DEPOSITED ON THE SEASHORE, VISHNU TURNED TO GARUDA.

THERE COMES VASUKI, BUT HE IS AFRAID TO COME CLOSER BE- CAUSE YOU ARE HIS NATURAL ENEMY. WITHDRAW, DEAR GARUDA, AND MAKE ROOM FOR THE KING OF SERPENTS.

WHEN HE SAW THAT GARUDA HAD FLOWN AWAY, VASUKI IMMEDIATELY OBEYED VISHNU'S SUMMONS.

PLAY YOUR ROLE WELL, VASUKI, AND YOU SHALL RECEIVE YOUR SHARE OF THE NECTAR. THE JAGGED SURFACE OF MANDARA SHALL NOT HURT YOU AT ALL.

REASSURED, VASUKI ALLOWED HIMSELF TO BE WOUND ROUND MANDARA.

THERE! NOW WE ARE READY. COME, FRIENDS AND BROTHERS, LET US CHURN WITH ALL OUR MIGHT FOR THE COMMON GOOD OF ALL OF US.

FULL OF JOYOUS ANTICIPATION, THEY BEGAN CHURNING.

BUT THEIR JOY SOON TURNED INTO DESPAIR. THE HEAVY MOUNT MANDARA, WHICH HAD NOTHING TO SUPPORT IT, SANK INTO THE OCEAN.

ALAS! IS THE NECTAR NEVER TO BE OURS?

WHAT IS TO BE DONE NOW?

IF WE, THE MIGHTIEST OF DEVAS AND ASURAS, COULD NOT HOLD UP MANDARA, WHO CAN?

THERE WAS ONE AND ONLY ONE WHO COULD — LORD VISHNU. TAKING THE FORM OF A HUGE TORTOISE...

...HE PLUNGED INTO THE OCEAN...

...AND TO THE AMAZED DELIGHT OF THE DEVAS AND ASURAS, CAME UP WITH THE MOUNTAIN ON HIS BACK.

IT IS THE LORD COME TO OUR AID AGAIN!

DO NOT WASTE TIME. ON WITH OUR TASK.

THEY CHURNED AND CHURNED, BUT IN VAIN.

I CANNOT CONTINUE ANY LONGER. MY LIMBS ARE NUMB!

I WILL HAVE TO DO THE CHURNING TOO.

THE FORCEFUL CHURNING FIRST THREW UP THE DEADLY POISON **HALA-HALA**, THE CONCENTRATE OF THE IMPURITIES OF THE OCEAN. ITS POISONOUS FUMES CHOKED THE DEVAS AND THE ASURAS.

OH! I CAN'T BREATHE!

I-I CAN'T SEE. I AM BLINDED.

FRIGHTENED OUT OF THEIR WITS, THEY RAN TO LORD SHIVA AT KAILASA.

GO IN PEACE. DO NOT FEAR. I SHALL TAKE IN THE POISON.

COLLECTING THE POISON INTO HIS PALM...

...SHIVA SWALLOWED IT.

AS SOON AS THE POISON WAS REMOVED, THE DEVAS AND ASURAS WERE ABLE TO CHURN THE OCEAN ONCE AGAIN.

AS THEY CONTINUED CHURNING, MANY PRECIOUS THINGS ROSE TO THE SURFACE, BUT NOT THE NECTAR. THEN SUDDENLY A BEING EMERGED —

WHO COULD HE BE!

IT WAS DHANWANTARI WITH THE JAR OF THE NECTAR OF IMMORTALITY —

THE JAR! IT CONTAINS THE NECTAR.

THE NECTAR.

SNATCH IT.

DON'T LET THE DEVAS GET AT IT.

FORGETTING THEIR TRUCE, THE ASURAS SNATCHED THE PRECIOUS JAR ALL FOR THEM-SELVES.

I SHALL HAVE IT FIRST.

NO, I SHALL.

NO. NOT YOU; I WILL.

GIVE IT TO ME. I AM YOUR CHIEF.

19

THE DEVAS WATCHED THE ASURAS IN DISMAY. BUT REMEMBERING VISHNU'S COMMAND THAT THEY SHOULD NOT QUARREL OVER WHAT THE OCEAN YIELDED, THEY MADE NO MOVE. VISHNU WAS PLEASED.

DO NOT BE DEJECTED. GREED FOR THE NECTAR HAS ALREADY DIVIDED THEM. NOW I SHALL CHARM THEM WITH MY POWERS AND GIVE YOU THE NECTAR.

THEN VISHNU TOOK ON THE FORM OF MOHINI, THE MOST BEAUTIFUL WOMAN EVER SEEN, AND APPROACHED THE ASURAS.

AH! WHAT A DAZZLING BEAUTY!

HOW PERFECT HER LIMBS!

HER EYES PIERCE MY BEING.

SO INFATUATED WERE THE ASURAS THAT THEY ENTRUSTED THE JAR OF NECTAR TO HER CARE.

PRAY, BEAUTIFUL ONE, DISTRIBUTE THE NECTAR SO THAT OUR QUARREL MAY END. BRING PEACE TO US.

MOHINI TOOK THE JAR. THEN—

I WILL DO SO IF YOU PROMISE NOT TO QUESTION MY ACTIONS.

NOT KNOWING WHO SHE REALLY WAS, THE ASURAS READILY AGREED.

THEN GO. BATHE AND ASSEMBLE IN THE MAIN HALL. YOU, THE ASURAS, IN ONE ROW AND YOUR COUSINS, THE DEVAS, IN ANOTHER.

WHEN THE DEVAS AND ASURAS HAD ASSEMBLED, MOHINI BEGAN SERVING THE NECTAR TO THE DEVAS. THE ASURAS WERE UNEASY.

THE NECTAR! WHAT IS SHE DOING?

HUSH! REMEMBER OUR PROMISE?

BESIDES, SHE IS A WOMAN. HOW CAN WE QUARREL WITH HER?

WE CAN'T. LET US AWAIT OUR TURN PATIENTLY.

BY THE TIME MOHINI REACHED THE END OF THE ROW OF DEVAS, SHE MADE SURE THAT THE NECTAR WAS EXHAUSTED.

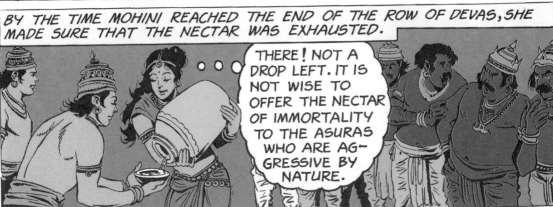

THERE! NOT A DROP LEFT. IT IS NOT WISE TO OFFER THE NECTAR OF IMMORTALITY TO THE ASURAS WHO ARE AGGRESSIVE BY NATURE.

THEN, TO THE AMAZEMENT OF THE ASURAS, LORD VISHNU ASSUMED HIS OWN FORM.

IT'S VISHNU! WE'VE BEEN DELUDED!

WHERE IS OUR SHARE OF THE NECTAR? THE NECTAR!

BUT VISHNU ONLY SMILED.

THEN MOUNTING GARUDA...

...HE FLEW AWAY INTO THE SKIES.

THE FURIOUS ASURAS CHARGED AT THE DEVAS.

WE HAVE BEEN TRICKED. DON'T SPARE THE SCOUNDRELS!

THE LORD IS ON OUR SIDE. WE HAVE DRUNK THE NECTAR OF IMMORTALITY. FIGHT ON.

CUT THEM UP.

THE GREAT DEVA-ASURA WAR THAT ENSUED THERE, ON THE SEASHORE, WAS A TERRIBLE ONE. BUT WITH HIS THUNDER-BOLT, INDRA, DESPITE THE SEVERAL REVERSES HE SUFFERED, WAS ABLE TO VANQUISH THE ASURAS.

MERCY!

MERCY!

FLEE!

FLEE!

MEANWHILE, BRAHMA SENT FOR SAGE NARADA —

INDRA HAS TASTED THE NECTAR OF IMMORTALITY AND HAS BEEN BLESSED BY LAXMI*. HIS MIGHT AND SPLENDOUR HAVE BEEN RESTORED TO HIM. THE ASURAS HAVE BEEN SUFFICIENTLY HUMBLED. GO. REQUEST HIM TO CEASE HOSTILITIES.

NARADA WENT TO INDRA AND CONVEYED BRAHMA'S MESSAGE.

THE GRANDSIRE IS RIGHT. LET US RETURN TO OUR REALMS.

AND THUS DID THE LORD REVIVE THE LOST GLORY OF THOSE WHO WERE GENTLE AND SOUGHT REFUGE IN HIM AND PUNISH THOSE WHO WERE AGGRESSIVE AND HAD NO FAITH IN HIM.

* THE GODDESS OF WEALTH.

VARAHA AVATAR

AFTER PRALAYA, AT THE BEGINNING OF THE NEW KALPA, WHILE BRAHMA WAS BUSY IN THE WORK OF CREATION...

...BHOOMIDEVI* BEING TOSSED ABOUT ON THE WAVES...

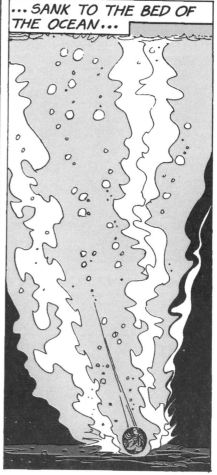

...SANK TO THE BED OF THE OCEAN...

*MOTHER EARTH

...AND SWAYAMBHUVA MANU AND SHATARUPA CAME INTO BEING.

THEY BOWED TO BRAHMA.

FATHER, TELL US HOW WE MAY SERVE YOU AS WELL AS ENSURE OUR HAPPINESS IN THIS WORLD AND THE NEXT.

KEEP YOUR HEART FREE FROM JEALOUSY, BEGET MANY VIRTUOUS CHILDREN AND RULE OVER THE EARTH, FOR YOU SHALL BE THE RULER OF MEN.

I SHALL OBEY YOUR WISHES. BUT PLEASE LET ME KNOW WHERE MY PROGENY AND I SHOULD LIVE. BHOOMIDEVI LIES SUBMERGED.

BRAHMA WAS TROUBLED.

WHAT SHALL I DO? I WILL HAVE TO BRING THE EARTH UP. O LORD VISHNU, PLEASE HELP ME.

AS BRAHMA MEDITATED ON THE LORD, A TINY BOAR, HARDLY AS BIG AS HIS THUMB, EMERGED FROM ONE OF HIS NOSTRILS.

WHAT IS THIS WEIRD CREATURE! AND COMING OUT OF MY NOSTRIL!

EVEN AS BRAHMA GAZED AT IT AMAZED, IT GREW...

...AND GREW...

...TILL IT WAS THE SIZE OF A LARGE ELEPHANT. BRAHMA WAS FULL OF WONDER.

COULD IT BE LORD VISHNU HIMSELF?

WHILE BRAHMA PONDERED THUS, THE BOAR, WHICH WAS NOW AS LARGE AS A HUGE MOUNTAIN, ROARED.

IT IS NONE OTHER THAN LORD VISHNU!

THEN, EMITTING ANOTHER TERRIFYING ROAR, IT TOOK ONE MIGHTY LEAP INTO THE AIR...

...TORE THE CLOUDS WITH ITS HOOFS...

...DIVED INTO THE OCEAN...

...AND NOSED ITS WAY ABOUT THE OCEAN-BED, IN SEARCH OF THE EARTH...

...TILL IT REACHED THE OTHER END OF THAT FATHOMLESS OCEAN AND DISCOVERED IN ITS DEPTHS...

...THE OBJECT OF ITS QUEST—BHOOMIDEVI.

MEANWHILE, THE MIGHTY ASURA, HIRANYAKSHA, THUNDERED UP TO HEAVEN, SPOILING FOR A COMBAT. BUT—

FIE ON THE LORD OF HEAVEN AND HIS DEVAS WHOM I HAVE SCARED INTO HIDING!

DISGUSTED AND ANGRY, HE MARCHED UP TO VARUNA, LORD OF THE WATERS AND FEIGNING HUMILITY, FELL AT HIS FEET.

O SUPREME LORD! O GUARDIAN OF A WHOLE SPHERE*! O RULER OF GREAT FAME! GIVE ME BATTLE.

HE MOCKS ME KNOWING FULLY WELL THAT HE IS THE MIGHTIER OF THE TWO.

BUT VARUNA CURBED HIS ANGER.

I HAVE GIVEN UP FIGHTING. I AM TOO OLD NOW. LORD VISHNU IS THE ONE YOU SHOULD APPROACH. HE ALONE WOULD BE AN EQUAL OPPONENT FOR YOU. GO SEEK HIM OUT.

LEARNING FROM THE SAGE NARADA WHERE VISHNU WAS, HIRANYAKSHA CHARGED TOWARDS THE OCEAN-BED.

* HYDROSPHERE.

MEANWHILE THE BOAR HAD JUST DUG HIS TUSK INTO THE OCEAN-BED...

...AND LIFTING BHOOMIDEVI ONTO IT...

...BEGUN RISING TOWARDS THE SURFACE, WHEN—

OH! SO HE IS NOW IN THE FORM OF A WILD BEAST!

HIRANYAKSHA CHALLENGED THE BEAST WITH A ROAR.

COME ON, YOU BEAST! LEAVE BHOOMIDEVI ALONE. SHE HAS BEEN ENTRUSTED TO US BY THE MAKER OF THE UNIVERSE.

WHEN THE BOAR IGNORED HIM —

YOU POSSESS LITTLE POWER. ALL YOUR BATTLES ARE WON BY YOGAMAYA*, YOUR ONLY STRENGTH. BUT NOW YOU ARE TOO CLOSE TO ESCAPE UNSCATHED.

THE BOAR CONTINUED RISING AND HIRANYAKSHA GAVE CHASE.

WAIT! AREN'T YOU ASHAMED OF YOURSELF? RUNNING AWAY FROM A FOE WHO CHALLENGES YOU!

BUT THE BOAR DID NOT EVEN LOOK BACK.

SHAMELESS WRETCH. THE SHARPEST INSULT FAILS TO PIERCE YOUR THICK HIDE.

LET HIM RAVE. MY TASK IS TO TAKE BHOOMIDEVI TO SAFETY. SHE TREMBLES WITH FRIGHT. AH! WE'VE ALMOST REACHED THE SURFACE.

✱ POWER OF ILLUSORY CREATION

AS SOON AS HE REACHED THE SURFACE OF THE OCEAN, HE PLACED BHOOMIDEVI GENTLY ON IT AND BLESSED HER.

MAY YOU SUPPORT YOURSELF IN KEEPING WITH THE DIVINE ORDER.

THEN HE TURNED TO FACE HIRANYAKSHA, HIS SPEECH HEAVY WITH SARCASM.

O WRETCH, SCARED AWAY BY YOUR MACE, WE WHO HAVE STOLEN THE EARTH MUST TAKE OUR STAND IN THE BATTLEFIELD. FOR, HAVING INCURRED THE WRATH OF A POWERFUL ENEMY, WHERE CAN WE GO?

HIRANYAKSHA BECAME FURIOUS. SEETHING WITH ANGER, HE LIFTED HIS MACE AND...

...SPRANG TOWARDS THE ANIMAL. BUT THE BOAR STEPPED ASIDE AND RAISED HIS OWN.

THEY FOUGHT FOR A LONG WHILE, EACH STRIKING OUT WITH HIS MACE.

AS THE HOUR OF TWILIGHT DREW NEAR, BRAHMA SPOKE TO THE BOAR.

SLAY HIM BEFORE HE GROWS FORMIDABLE WITH THE APPROACH OF AN HOUR THAT IS FAVOURABLE TO HIM. SLAY HIM AND RID US OF THIS PESTILENCE.

HEARING BRAHMA'S WORDS, HIRANYAKSHA HURLED HIS MACE AT THE ANIMAL.

THE MACE WAS CAUGHT BY THE BOAR AS IF IT WERE A TOY.

ENRAGED, HIRANYAKSHA BEGAN HITTING OUT WITH HIS FISTS ON THE CHEST OF THE BOAR.

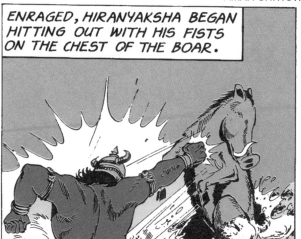

THE BOAR PLAYFULLY HIT THE DEMON BEHIND HIS EARS.

HIRANYAKSHA REELED AND FELL DEAD.

O LORD, ONLY YOU IN YOUR IMMACULATE GOODNESS COULD HAVE LIFTED BHOO-MIDEVI TO THE SURFACE OF THE OCEAN. ONLY YOUR INVINCIBLE SELF COULD HAVE SAVED US FROM THIS SCOURGE.

NARASIMHA AVATAR

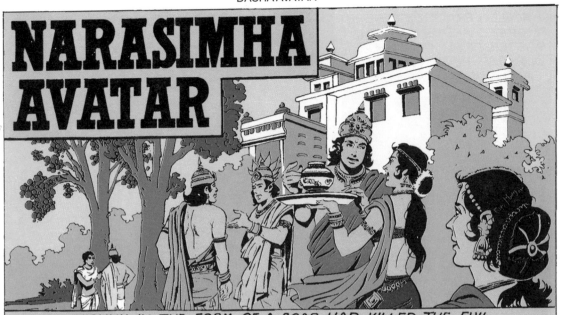

VISHNU, IN THE FORM OF A BOAR, HAD KILLED THE EVIL ASURA, HIRANYAKSHA. THE DEVAS WERE HAPPY AND THERE WAS MUCH REJOICING IN HEAVEN AND ON EARTH, BUT NOT FOR LONG.

HIRANYAKASHIPU, HIRANYAKSHA'S ELDER BROTHER, SEETHING WITH ANGER, WAS BENT ON AVENGING THE DEATH OF HIS BROTHER.

VISHNU THRIVES ON VIRTUOUS SOULS AND THEIR VIR- TUOUS DEEDS.

HE TURNED TO THE ASURAS WHO HAD COME TO OFFER HIM THEIR CONDOLENCES.

GO. DESTROY ALL GOOD PEOPLE ON EARTH. PUT OUT THEIR SACRIFICIAL FIRES AND KILL THEIR COWS...

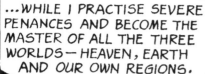

...WHILE I PRACTISE SEVERE PENANCES AND BECOME THE MASTER OF ALL THE THREE WORLDS—HEAVEN, EARTH AND OUR OWN REGIONS.

THEN SHALL I EXALT SIN AND SUBDUE VIRTUE. I SHALL DRIVE THE DEVAS AND THE SAGES TO THE NETHER REGIONS AND THROW OPEN HEAVEN, THE HIGHEST SPHERE, TO THE ASURAS.

AND HIRANYAKASHIPU WENT TO MOUNT MANDARA AND BEGAN HIS PENANCES.

SO HE STOOD FOR YEARS AND YEARS.

ANT HILLS AND GRASS GREW ON HIS PERSON BUT HE DID NOT MOVE.

THE RIVERS AND OCEANS TREMBLED —

THE DAY OF BRAHMA MUST BE OVER. THE HOUR OF DISSOLUTION IS COME.

THE EARTH AND HER MOUNTAINS QUAKED...

...AND THE STARS AND PLANETS DARTED ABOUT IN PANIC.

SO INTENSE WAS HIRANYAKASHIPU'S PENANCE THAT THE FIERY SMOKE EMERGING FROM HIS HEAD BEGAN TO SCORCH EVERYTHING IN ITS WAKE.

THE DEVAS WERE TERRIFIED. LED BY INDRA, THEY WENT TO BRAHMA, THE CREATOR.

O MERCIFUL LORD, PRAY DO SOMETHING, ANYTHING, BEFORE THE THREE WORLDS OF YOUR CREATION ARE CONSUMED BY THE FIRE OF THE ASURA'S PENANCES.

MOVED BY THEIR PLIGHT, BRAHMA WENT TO MOUNT MANDARA. A FEW SAGES ACCOMPANIED HIM.

ENOUGH, O ASURA. ARISE. I HAVE BEEN CONQUERED BY YOUR AUSTERITIES. ANY BOON YOU SEEK SHALL BE YOURS.

THE HOLY WATER FROM THE CREATOR'S KAMANDALU REJUVENATED THE ASURA. HE EMERGED, HANDSOME AND RADIANT.

LET NOT DEATH COME TO ME EITHER BY MAN OR BEAST, BY DAY OR BY NIGHT, INDOORS OR OUTDOORS, ON EARTH OR IN THE SKY. GRANT ME UNDISPUTED LORDSHIP OVER THE MATERIAL WORLD.

SO BE IT.

ARMED WITH THE BOONS, THE ASURA LOST NO TIME IN CONQUERING AND BRINGING UNDER HIS SWAY, BOTH HEAVEN AND EARTH.

I WISH TO OCCUPY THE PALACE OF THE LORD OF THE DEVAS. DRIVE HIM OUT.

BETRAYED BY BRAHMA, THE DEVAS APPROACHED VISHNU THE PRESERVER. VISHNU'S VOICE REASSURED THEM.

HAVE PATIENCE, O DEVAS. I KNOW THE EVIL THAT IS THE ASURA. HIS SON, THE HIGH-SOULED PRAHLAD* IS DEVOTED TO ME. WHEN THE ASURA SEEKS TO KILL MY DEVOTEE, I SHALL SLAY HIM.

THE DEVAS DID NOT HAVE TO WAIT LONG. EVEN AS VISHNU MADE HIS PROMISE, HIRANYAKASHIPU WAS SCREAMING WITH EXASPERATION AT HIS SON.

YOU WILL INSIST ON DEFYING ME AND WOR-SHIPPING MY SWORN ENEMY, ME, BEFORE WHOM THE DENIZENS OF ALL THE THREE WORLDS QUAKE WITH FEAR!

DEEP IN CONTEMPLATION OF LORD VISHNU, PRAHLAD DID NOT UTTER A WORD. HIRANYAKASHIPU ROARED IN FURY.

YOU SEEM TO BE CONFIDENT IN YOUR FAITH. O FOOL, I CAN-NOT IMAGINE WHERE YOU GET THE STRENGTH FROM!

* SEE AMAR CHITRA KATHA NO.537—PRAHLAD

AT LAST PRAHLAD SPOKE.

FROM WHOM NOT ONLY I BUT ALSO YOU AND ALL OTHER POWERFUL BEINGS DERIVE THEIRS — THE ALL-PERVADING LORD VISHNU.

HIRANYAKASHIPU BECAME LIVID WITH RAGE.

IF HE IS ALL-PERVADING, HE MUST BE IN THIS PILLAR. I AM GOING TO SLAY YOU NOW. LET HIM COME AND PROTECT...

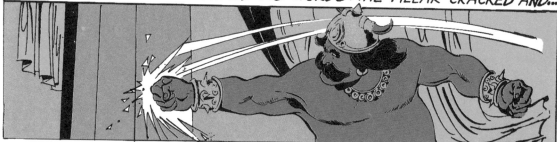

A RESOUNDING CRASH DROWNED HIS WORDS. THE PILLAR CRACKED AND...

... LORD VISHNU IN THE FORM OF NARASIMHA* EMERGED AND SUBSTANTIATED HIS DEVOTEE'S WORDS.

HE IS NEITHER A BEAST NOR A HUMAN BEING. WHAT MIGHT THIS STRANGE CREATURE BE?

* MAN-LION

AS NARASIMHA ADVANCED MENACINGLY UPON HIM, HIRANYAKASHIPU TRIED TO REGAIN HIS COMPOSURE.

IT MUST BE VISHNU. HE HAS TAKEN THIS FORM TO KILL ME. HE MAY HAVE TAKEN CARE OF ONE CONDITION BUT HE STILL CANNOT HARM ME.

EMBOLDENED BY THAT THOUGHT, THE ASURA PICKED UP A MACE AND...

...ROARING LOUDLY RUSHED AT NARASIMHA.

BUT AS HE CAME NEAR, NARASIMHA SEIZED HIM, MACE AND ALL, IN A CLOSE EMBRACE.

HIRANYAKSHIPU HOWEVER SLIPPED THROUGH HIS ARMS...

...AND GRABBING A SWORD...

...CHARGED ONCE AGAIN.

WATCHING HIS MOVEMENTS, NARASIMHA SENT FORTH A SHRILL PEAL OF LAUGHTER FOLLOWED BY A WEIRD ROAR.

AND THE NEXT MOMENT, THE ASURA FOUND HIMSELF IN THE VICE-LIKE GRIP OF NARASIMHA'S CLAWS.

IT IS THE TWILIGHT HOUR! NEITHER DAY NOR NIGHT...

NARASIMHA CARRIED THE ASURA TO THE THRESHOLD OF THE HALL.

WE ARE NEITHER INDOORS NOR OUTDOORS!

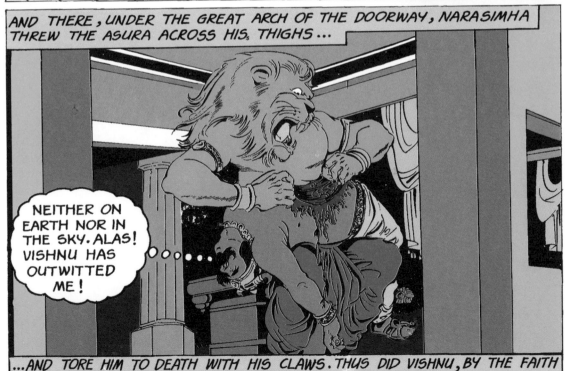

AND THERE, UNDER THE GREAT ARCH OF THE DOORWAY, NARASIMHA THREW THE ASURA ACROSS HIS THIGHS...

NEITHER ON EARTH NOR IN THE SKY. ALAS! VISHNU HAS OUTWITTED ME!

...AND TORE HIM TO DEATH WITH HIS CLAWS. THUS DID VISHNU, BY THE FAITH OF HIS DEVOTEE, PREVENT THE TRIUMPH OF EVIL AND ESTABLISH VIRTUE.

VAMANA AVATAR

BENT ON CONQUERING THE DEVAS, BALI*, THE KING OF THE ASURAS, GUIDED BY SHUKRACHARYA, HIS PRECEPTOR, PERFORMED THE VISHWAJIT SACRIFICE**...

...AND RECEIVED FROM THE SACRIFICIAL FIRE A GOLDEN CHARIOT, CELESTIAL WEAPONS AND A COAT OF MAIL, FOR THE CONQUEST OF HEAVEN.

* GRANDSON OF PRAHLAD.
** A SACRIFICE PERFORMED TO GAIN MASTERY OVER THE THREE WORLDS.

DONNING THE ARMOUR, BALI MOUNTED THE CHARIOT AND WITH HIS ASURA HORDES ADVANCED ON AMARAVATI, THE CAPITAL OF THE DEVAS.

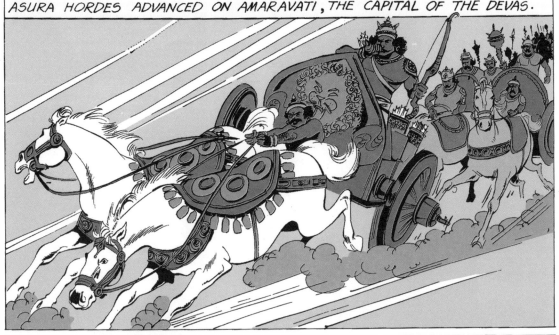

IN THE PALACE OF INDRA, KING OF THE DEVAS—

WHAT A TERRIBLE UPROAR!

THE SOUND FILLS THE SKIES AND SHAKES THE WORLDS.

IT IS BALI! HE IS SURROUNDING OUR CITY!

AS BALI LAID SIEGE TO THE CITY, INDRA WENT TO BRIHASPATI, HIS PRECEPTOR.

WHAT SHOULD WE DO, O VENERABLE ONE? BALI IS NOW RIDING SOME STRANGE POWER. WE MAY FAIL IN BEATING HIM BACK.

BRIHASPATI NODDED WISELY.

YOU ARE RIGHT. BALI AT THE MOMENT IS INVINCIBLE. I WOULD ADVISE YOU TO RETREAT FROM HEAVEN TILL THE TIDE TURNS IN YOUR FAVOUR.

AND WHEN WILL THAT BE?

WHEN HIS GURU CURSES HIM FOR IGNORING HIS COUNSEL.

SO, INDRA AND THE DEVAS ABANDONED HEAVEN; AND BALI PROMPTLY OCCUPIED IT WITH HIS ASURA HORDES.

I AM NOW THE LORD OF ALL THE THREE WORLDS!

MEANWHILE, ADITI, THE MOTHER OF THE DEVAS, SAT BROODING ABOUT THEIR SORRY PLIGHT. SAGE KASHYAP, HER HUSBAND, WAS AWAY IN THE FOREST, MEDITATING.

IF ONLY MY LORD WERE HERE.

JUST THEN KASHYAP ENTERED THE HERMITAGE.

THE HERMITAGE LOOKS DESOLATE AND ADITI DISTRESSED. I HOPE ALL IS WELL.

AH, MY LORD! YOU HAVE RETURNED.

WHAT IS THE MATTER? IS ALL WELL WITH YOU AND YOUR SONS?

NO, MY LORD. THE ASURAS HAVE USURPED OUR KINGDOM AND WITH IT, OUR SPLENDOUR AND OUR GLORY. YOU MUST HELP MY SONS TO RETRIEVE THEIR LOST STATUS.

IT IS NOT ME THAT YOU SHOULD APPEAL TO, BUT THE ALL-PERVADING LORD VISHNU. HE AND HE ALONE CAN HELP YOU. PROPITIATE HIM.

TELL ME THE QUICKEST MEANS OF DOING IT, MY LORD. I CANNOT BEAR THE MISERY OF MY SONS ANY LONGER.

DURING THE BRIGHT HALF OF THE MONTH OF PHALGUNA, WITH YOUR MIND FIXED ON THE LORD, OBSERVE THE PAYOVRATA*VOW THE VOW THAT GRATIFIES HIM THE MOST. PLEASED, HE WILL GRANT YOUR DESIRES.

FOCUSSING HER MIND ON VISHNU, ADITI OBSERVED THE VOW OF TWELVE LONG DAYS. ON THE THIRTEENTH DAY—

INVINCIBLE THOUGH THE ASURAS ARE, O DIVINE LADY, YOUR WORSHIP SHALL NOT PROVE FRUITLESS. I SHALL ASSUME THE ROLE OF A SON TO YOU AND PROTECT YOUR PROGENY.

* VOW OF MILK (NOTHING BUT MILK SHOULD BE DRUNK BY THOSE WHO OBSERVE THIS VOW.)

MONTHS LATER, ON THE TWELFTH DAY OF THE BRIGHT HALF OF BHADRAPADA,* VISHNU TOOK HIS DESCENT FROM ADITI.

THEN, EVEN WHILE THE COUPLE STOOD GAZING, VISHNU CHANGED HIS FORM...

...TO THAT OF A SHORT-STATURED BRAHMAN.

A FEW DAYS LATER, A BLINDING LIGHT FILLED THE SACRIFICIAL GROUNDS WHERE BALI WAS PERFORMING A SERIES OF HORSE SACRIFICES.

COULD IT BE LORD SURYA** HIMSELF COME DOWN TO WITNESS OUR SACRIFICE?

*THE SIXTH MONTH OF THE HINDU CALENDAR

**THE SUN GOD

AS THEIR EYES GOT USED TO THE BRILLIANCE, THEY SAW THAT A BRAHMAN MIDGET HAD ENTERED THE SACRIFICIAL ENCLOSURE.

BALI ROSE FROM HIS SEAT TO RECEIVE HIM.

WELCOME, O HOLY BRAHMAN. THIS LAND OF MINE HAS BEEN CON-SECRATED BY YOUR TINY FEET.

THEN HE GAVE THE DIVINE MIDGET, VAMANA, A SPECIAL SEAT AND WASHED HIS FEET.

O HOLY ONE, WHAT CAN I DO FOR YOU? PRAY TAKE FROM ME WHAT-EVER YOU DESIRE.

VAMANA WAS QUIET:

DO NOT HESITATE, O BRAHMACHARI.* WHAT WILL YOU HAVE — A COW, GOLD, ELEPHANTS, HORSES, CHARIOTS, A BRIDE, A PALATIAL HOUSE, PROS-PEROUS VILLAGES...?

* CELIBATE.

VAMANA SHOOK HIS HEAD.

ALL I SEEK IS A STRIP OF LAND, THREE PACES LONG AS MEASURED BY MY STRIDE.

SEEKING TO WIN ACCLAIM FOR HIS GENEROSITY, BALI WAS DISAPPOINTED WITH VAMANA'S HUMBLE DEMAND.

YOU ARE TOO YOUNG TO BE ALIVE TO YOUR OWN INTEREST. WHEN I AM READY TO GRANT YOU A WHOLE CON- TINENT, YOU WANT BUT THREE PACES OF LAND.

HE WHO CANNOT BE SATISFIED WITH THREE PACES OF LAND WILL NOT BE SATISFIED EVEN WITH A WHOLE CONTINENT.

THREE PACES OF LAND ARE ALL I NEED AND THREE PACES OF LAND ARE ALL THAT I WILL HAVE.

BALI LAUGHED AND GAVE IN.

THEN YOU SHALL HAVE AS MUCH.

AT THAT MOMENT SHUKRA-CHARYA REALISED THE TRUTH.

HE IS NONE OTHER THAN LORD VISHNU.

AS BALI TOOK THE CONSECRATING WATER IN HIS PALM, SHUKRACHARYA STOPPED HIM.

WAIT! THIS MIDGET IS LORD VISHNU. HE IS HERE TO HELP OUR ENEMIES, THE DEVAS.

NOTHING CAN BE DONE NOW, O VENERABLE ONE. I HAVE GIVEN MY WORD.

RETRACT IT. IT IS NOT WRONG TO DO SO WHEN ONE'S LIFE AND THE LIVES OF ONE'S DEPENDANTS ARE AT STAKE.

BALI WAS QUIET FOR A MOMENT. THEN—

HAVING PROMISED ONCE THAT I SHALL GIVE, HOW CAN I, BALI, THE GRANDSON OF VIRTUOUS PRAHLAD, REFUSE LIKE A COMMON CHEAT? I WILL GIVE THIS BRAHMAN THE LAND HE SEEKS, O HOLY SAGE, COME WHAT MAY.

FURIOUS THAT HIS DISCIPLE HAD DARED TO DISREGARD HIS ADVICE, SHUKRACHARYA CURSED HIM.

HAVE YOU GROWN SO ARROGANT AS TO IGNORE MY COMMAND? CONCEITED FOOL THAT YOU ARE, YOU WILL SOON FALL FROM YOUR HIGH POSITION.

BALI'S WIFE THEN CAME WITH A GOLDEN PITCHER FULL OF WATER TO WASH VAMANA'S FEET.

AND LO! VAMANA BEGAN TO GROW...

...AND GROW. BALI AND ALL THE SAGES PRESENT WERE ASTOUNDED TO SEE THE WHOLE OF CREATION IN VAMANA'S BODY...

...AS HE BEGAN TO MEASURE THE THREE PACES. WITH HIS FIRST STRIDE HE COVERED THE EARTH...

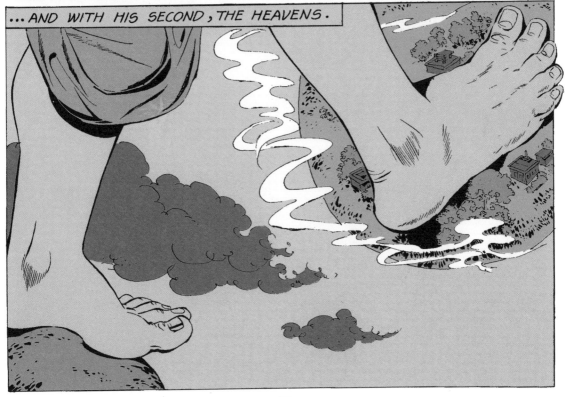

...AND WITH HIS SECOND, THE HEAVENS.

THE ENRAGED ASURAS TOOK UP ARMS AND RAN TOWARDS HIM.

HE IS NO BRAHMAN. IT IS VISHNU HIMSELF, OUT TO DELUDE US!

BUT BALI STOPPED THEM.

I HAVE BEEN CURSED BY MY GURU. MY FALL IS INEVITABLE.

PRAY DO NOT MAKE WAR. RETREAT.

AS THE ASURAS RETREATED TO THE NETHER WORLD, GARUDA BOUND BALI WITH ROPES...

...AND TOOK HIM TO VISHNU.

THOUGH CURSED BY HIS PRECEPTOR, THIS GREAT SOUL DID NOT GO BACK ON HIS WORD. I MUST TEST HIM FURTHER AND ENHANCE HIS REPUTATION FOR BEING STEADFAST.

WITH THAT INTENTION VISHNU SPOKE HARSH WORDS TO HIM.

YOU PROMISED ME THREE PACES OF LAND AND I HAVE COVERED ALL THAT WAS YOURS IN TWO. YOU HAVE FAILED TO KEEP YOUR WORD. YOU WILL HAVE TO SUFFER FOR IT.

BALI WAS UNPERTURBED.

O ILLUSTRIOUS ONE, I AM NOT AFRAID OF PUNISHMENT AT YOUR HANDS AS I AM OF BEING CALLED IGNOBLE. I HAD NO INTENTION OF DECEIVING YOU.

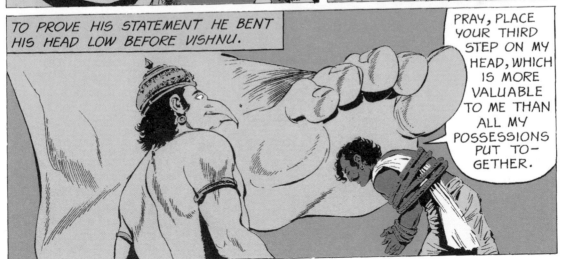

TO PROVE HIS STATEMENT HE BENT HIS HEAD LOW BEFORE VISHNU.

PRAY, PLACE YOUR THIRD STEP ON MY HEAD, WHICH IS MORE VALUABLE TO ME THAN ALL MY POSSESSIONS PUT TOGETHER.

AT THAT MOMENT, PRAHLAD APPEARED ON THE SCENE AND BOWED LOW TO VISHNU —

SALUTATIONS TO YOU, O LORD. YOU HAVE CONFERRED A GREAT FAVOUR ON MY GRANDSON BY DEPRIVING HIM OF HIS WEALTH. FOR, WEALTH CORRUPTS EVEN GREAT SOULS.

BUT NOT YOUR GRANDSON'S SOUL. HE STOOD FIRM BY HIS PROMISE EVEN AT THE COST OF DISOBEYING HIS GURU AND INVITING HIS CURSE. HE REMAINS SERENE, EVEN IN THE FACE OF THE CALAMITY WHICH HAS BEFALLEN HIM.

HE HAS ALL BUT EARNED ENTRY INTO MY OWN REALMS WHICH EVEN THE DEVAS FIND DIFFICULT OF ACCESS. BUT FIRST HE WILL ENJOY FOR A WHOLE MANVANTARA THE POSITION OF INDRA AS HE DESIRED IT.

THUS DID VISHNU IN HIS VAMANA AVATAR BEG THE EARTH AND THE HEAVENS FOR THE DEVAS FROM THEIR ENEMY, THE RIGHTEOUS BUT VAIN KING OF THE ASURAS.

PARASHURAMA AVATAR

KING ARJUNA, THE RULER OF THE HAIHAYAS, HAD PROPITIATED LORD DATTATREYA AND HAD SECURED FROM HIM BOONS WHICH MADE HIM INVINCIBLE. BUT ARJUNA MISUSED HIS POWERS AND BECAME A MERCILESS TYRANT.

TO VANQUISH HIM AND ALL SUCH EVIL KSHATRIYAS, LORD VISHNU CAME TO EARTH AS RAMA, THE YOUNGEST SON OF SAGE JAMADAGNI, AND HIS WIFE, RENUKA.

IT'S STRANGE THAT MY SON SHOULD KNOW SO MUCH ABOUT WEAPONS AND THEIR USE.

IT WAS TRUE. THOUGH RAMA WAS THE SON OF A BRAHMAN, HE HAD AN INORDINATE LOVE FOR WEAPONS AND HIS FAVOURITE WAS THE AXE.

ONE DAY, WHILE PARASHURAMA* AND HIS BROTHERS WERE AWAY, ARJUNA ENTERED JAMADAGNI'S HERMITAGE.

WELCOME, O MIGHTY KING. REST HERE WITH YOUR MEN AND TASTE THE YIELD OF KAMADHENU.

BUT WHEN ARJUNA AND HIS MEN WERE FED—

IF KAMADHENU CAN FEED SO MANY IN SUCH A SHORT TIME, I MUST POSSESS HER.

HE TURNED TO HIS MEN.

SEIZE THE ANIMAL AND HER YOUNG ONE. TAKE THEM TO MY CAPITAL.

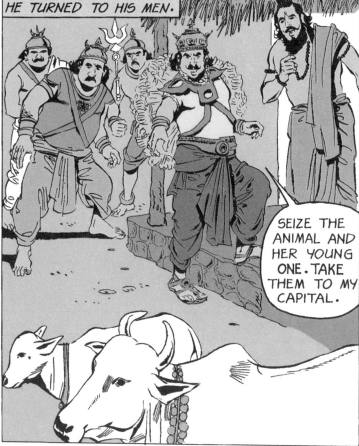

*SEE AMAR CHITRA KATHA NO.764 - PARASHURAMA

A FEW DAYS LATER, WHEN PARASHURAMA RETURNED TO THE HERMITAGE —

O RAMA, THE KING HAS TAKEN AWAY MY BELOVED KAMA-DHENU AND HER CALF.

HOW DARE HE COMMIT SUCH A SACRILEGE! I SHALL DEAL WITH HIM.

BRANDISHING HIS AXE, AN ENRAGED PARASHURAMA STORMED INTO MAHISHMATI, ARJUNA'S CAPITAL. ARJUNA WAS ALARMED.

IT'S PARASHURAMA! SEND OUT SEVENTEEN OF OUR MOST POWERFUL AKSHAUHINIS* TO MEET HIM.

BUT THE TERRIBLE PARASHURAMA DESTROYED THEM IN NO TIME. NOT A SINGLE MAN ESCAPED ALIVE.

*AN AKSHAUHINI CONSITED OF 1,09,350 INFANTRY, 65,610 CAVALRY, 21,870 CHARIOTS AND AN EQUAL NUMBER OF ELEPHANTS.

ENRAGED AT THE DESTRUCTION OF THE CORE OF HIS ARMY, ARJUNA HIMSELF RUSHED FORWARD. BUT —

AS ARJUNA RUSHED TOWARDS HIM WITH UPROOTED TREES AND ROCKS, PARASHURAMA LOPPED OFF ALL HIS ARMS...

...AND THEN BROUGHT HIS AXE DOWN ON THE TYRANT'S NECK.

PARASHURAMA THEN LED KAMADHENU AND HER CALF TO HIS FATHER.

AND LIFE IN THE HERMITAGE WENT ON AS BEFORE.

BUT NOT FOR LONG. THE SONS OF ARJUNA WERE BENT ON AVENGING THE DEATH OF THEIR FATHER. ONE DAY, WHILE PARASHURAMA WAS AWAY IN THE WOODS...

LORD!

...THEY FELL UPON THE SAGE AND CUT OFF HIS HEAD.

NO! SPARE MY HUSBAND! PLEASE SPARE HIM!

RAMA! OH RAMA!

MEANWHILE, PARASHURAMA WAS ON HIS WAY BACK TO THE HERMITAGE. SUDDENLY —

THAT CRY! IT'S MY MOTHER'S. SHE SEEMS TO BE IN DISTRESS. I MUST HASTEN TO HER SIDE.

WHEN PARASHURAMA REACHED THE HERMITAGE, HE WAS AGHAST.

MOTHER! WHO WERE THE FOUL MURDERERS? TELL ME, MOTHER!

RAMA! OH RAMA! RAMA!

BUT RENUKA'S AGONY WAS SO DEEP THAT SHE COULD ONLY BEAT HER BREAST AND CRY. FULL OF GRIEF AND ANGER, PARASHURAMA MADE A VOW.

TWENTY-ONE TIMES HAVE YOU BEATEN YOUR BREAST, MOTHER. I SHALL WIPE OUT THE VILE RACE OF THE KSHATRIYAS AS MANY TIMES.

AND, GRIPPING HIS AXE, PARASHURAMA SET OUT TO ACCOMPLISH THE REST OF THE TASK FOR WHICH HE HAD COME TO EARTH.

THUS DID LORD VISHNU, AS PARASHURAMA, EXTERMINATE THOSE KSHATRIYAS WHO HAD BECOME A GREAT BURDEN TO BHOOMIDEVI AND HER CHILDREN.

RAMA AVATAR

RAVANA*, THE ARROGANT RAKSHASA KING OF THE ISLAND OF LANKA, HAD PERFORMED SEVERE PENANCES AND HAD SECURED BOONS WHICH MADE HIM ALL BUT IMMORTAL.

PERTURBED BY THE ATROCITIES COMMITTED BY THE RAKSHASA, THE DEVAS APPROACHED VISHNU FOR PROTECTION.

HE NOW PLANS TO INVADE OUR VERY REGIONS.

VISHNU REASSURED THEM.

DO NOT WORRY. TO SLAY HIM I SHALL MANIFEST MYSELF ON EARTH AS THE FOUR SONS OF DASHA-RATHA—WHOLLY IN RAMA, THE ELDEST, AND PARTIALLY IN HIS BROTHERS.

✱ SEE AMAR CHITRA KATHA NO. 541 — THE LORD OF LANKA

ACCORDINGLY, FOUR SONS WERE BORN TO THE THREE QUEENS OF DASHARATHA,*THE HEIRLESS KING OF AYODHYA. RAMA*THE ELDEST, TO KAUSALYA; BHARATA ,TO KAIKEYI; AND LAXMANA AND SHATRUGHNA ,TO SUMITRA.

RAMA WILL MAKE AN IDEAL KING. HE IS VIRTUOUS. AND VALIANT.

BUT, A FEW YEARS LATER, INSTEAD OF CROWNING HIM YUVARAJA, A HEARTBROKEN DASHARATHA, BOUND BY A PROMISE ,WAS COMPELLED TO BANISH RAMA TO THE FOREST FOR FOURTEEN YEARS. SITA, RAMA'S YOUNG WIFE, AND LAXMANA INSISTED ON GOING WITH HIM.

FORGIVE ME, RAMA! FORGIVE ME, SITA.

WHILE THEY WERE IN THE FOREST —

NOBLE SIR, I,SHOORPANAKHA, KING RAVANA'S SISTER, WISH TO MAKE YOU MY OWN.

*SEE AMAR CHITRA KATHA NO. 570 —DASHARATHA AND NO.504—RAMA.

THOUGH AMUSED, RAMA KEPT A STRAIGHT FACE.

BUT I AM NOT FREE. I BELONG TO SITA.

HIS WORDS TRANSFORMED SHOORPANAKHA.

SHE CHARGED MENACINGLY TOWARDS SITA. BUT LAXMANA WAS TOO QUICK FOR HER.

HE SPRANG FORWARD AND HACKED OFF HER NOSE AND EARS.

A TEARFUL, DISFIGURED SHOOR-PANAKHA STOOD BEFORE RAVANA.

SINCE THEIR LOVE FOR SITA MADE THEM DO THIS TO YOU, I SHALL PUNISH THEM BY ABDUCTING HER FOR MYSELF.

RAVANA TOOK THE HELP OF HIS UNCLE MAREECHA.

I WILL NOT RISK AN OPEN ENCOUNTER WITH THE BROTHERS. TRANSFORM YOURSELF INTO A GOLDEN DEER AND LURE THEM AWAY. IN THEIR ABSENCE I WILL CARRY SITA AWAY.

RAVANA'S RUSE WORKED AND BEFORE LONG—

O LORD! SAVE ME!

IN THE DAYS THAT FOLLOWED WHILE RAMA AND LAXMANA WANDERED IN THE FOREST NOT KNOWING WHERE TO LOOK FOR SITA, THEY WON THE AFFECTION OF SUGREEVA,* THE KING OF THE MONKEYS.

WE SHALL HELP YOU FIND SITA, WHEREVER SHE MAY BE.

*SEE AMAR CHITRA KATHA NO. 546 —VALI

HANUMAN*, HIS MINISTER, WENT ON THE ERRAND AND CAME BACK WITH THE NEWS THAT SITA WAS AT LANKA.

POOR SITA! LET US MARCH TO THE SEA-SHORE WITH YOUR FORCES, SUGREEVA.

AT THE SEASHORE —

HOW SHALL WE CROSS THIS MIGHTY OCEAN?

THE LORD OF THE OCEAN WILL HELP US

RAMA WAITED FOR THREE DAYS WITH-OUT HAVING ANY FOOD OR WATER. AT LAST, VARUNA APPEARED AND IMMEDIATELY KNEW HIM TO BE VISHNU.

O LORD, PARDON MY IGNORANCE. YOU CAN MARCH ACROSS MY DOMAIN AT WILL BUT...

*SEE AMAR CHITRA KATHA NO. 502 - HANUMAN

...ENHANCE YOUR OWN FAME BY BUILDING A BRIDGE ACROSS ME FOR WHICH POSTERITY WILL SING YOUR GLORY.

ASSISTED BY THE MONKEYS AND OTHER CREATURES OF THE FOREST, A BRIDGE WAS SOON LAID BY RAMA AND LAXMANA, ACROSS THE SEAS TO THE SHORE OF LANKA.

AS RAVANA SAW THE TWO BROTHERS AND THEIR HORDES APPROACH, HE SENT FOR HIS SON, HIS BROTHER AND HIS FOREMOST WARRIORS.

GO! MEET THE INVADING ARMY AND DEFEAT IT!

BUT RAMA, SUGREEVA, LAXMANA, HANUMAN AND THEIR WILD HORDES EFFORTLESSLY DESTROYED RAVANA'S HUGE ARMY OF ELEPHANTS, CAVALRY, INFANTRY AND CHARIOTS, IN A SINGLE ENCOUNTER!

RAVANA WAS FURIOUS. HE RUSHED TOWARDS RAMA. BUT —

O VILE RAKSHASA, REAP TODAY THE FRUITS OF YOUR VILLAINY.

AND WITH ONE TWANG OF HIS BOW...

...VISHNU, AS RAMA, COMPLETED THE MISSION FOR WHICH HE HAD TAKEN HIS BIRTH ON EARTH.

KRISHNA AVATAR

ON THE EVE OF THE DAWN OF THE KALI YUGA, MANY TYRANTS LIKE KAMSA (AND THE DEMONS IN HIS PAY), JARASANDHA, SHISHUPALA, THE KAURAVAS AND THEIR HORDES, MOLESTED BHOOMIDEVI OFTEN IN THE ROLES OF ARROGANT KINGS.

DISTRESSED, SHE STOOD BEFORE BRAHMA IN THE FORM OF A DISCONSOLATE COW.

I SEEK REFUGE IN YOU, O LORD. RID ME OF MY BURDEN.

WHEN BRAHMA IN TURN PRAYED TO VISHNU FOR GUIDANCE—

I KNOW OF BHOOMI DEVI'S DISTRESS. SHESHA* AND I SHALL COME DOWN AS THE SEVENTH AND EIGHTH SONS OF VASUDEVA TO FREE HER OF HER BURDEN. THE DEVAS, MEANWHILE, SHOULD PRECEDE US AS VIRTUOUS MEN AND AWAIT OUR DESCENT.

*THE SERPENT ON WHOM VISHNU RESTS.

AT THAT MOMENT, VASUDEVA, A YADAVA NOBLEMAN OF MATHURA, WAS GETTING MARRIED TO DEVAKI, KING UGRASENA'S NIECE.

LATER, WHEN UGRASENA'S SON, KAMSA, AFFECTIONATELY TOOK THE REINS TO DRIVE THE COUPLE'S CHARIOT, AN ORACLE SPOKE FROM THE SKIES.

O FOOLISH KAMSA, THE EIGHTH SON OF THIS VERY GIRL IS DESTINED TO SLAY YOU.

AN ENRAGED KAMSA SEIZED DEVAKI BY THE HAIR AND RAISED HIS SWORD TO BRING IT DOWN ON HER...

...WHEN A HAND STOPPED HIM.

IT BELONGED TO THE GENTLE VASUDEVA.

I PROMISE TO HAND OVER TO YOU EVERY CHILD BORN TO HER. LET HER LIVE.

AND I WILL CLING TO THE HOPE THAT DIVINE INTERVENTION WILL SAVE OUR OFFSPRING WHEN THE TIME COMES.

KAMSA AGREED AND THE PROCESSION MOVED ON.

BUT, TERRIFIED BY THE PREDICTION, KAMSA IMPRISONED UGRASENA AND ASSUMING ALL POWER, BECAME THE RULER OF MATHURA.

THOUGH I TOO AM A YADAVA, SINCE A YADAVA IS DESTINED TO BE MY KILLER, I SHALL PERSECUTE AND DESTROY THE RACE.

MEANWHILE, TRUE TO HIS WORD, VASUDEVA HANDED OVER TO KAMSA'S MEN THE FIRST SIX SONS BORN TO DEVAKI.

PUT THE VILE INFANT TO DEATH.

WHEN THE SEVENTH CHILD WAS ABOUT TO BE BORN, VISHNU'S DIVINE POWER, YOGAMAYA APPEARED.

AS ORDERED BY THE LORD, I HAVE TO TRANSFER THE CHILD, BALARAMA, TO THE WOMB OF ROHINI, VASUDEVA'S WIFE AT GOKUL.

THIS WAS TO MISLEAD KAMSA INTO BELIEVING THAT DEVAKI HAD LOST HER SEVENTH CHILD.

AFTER ACCOMPLISHING HER TASK —

NOW, I MUST ENTER THE WOMB OF YASHODA, THE WIFE OF NANDA* AND AWAIT THE DESCENT OF THE LORD.

A FEW MONTHS LATER, LORD VISHNU APPEARED BEFORE THE AWESTRUCK DEVAKI AND VASUDEVA.

VASUDEVA, TAKE ME TO GOKUL AND LEAVE ME IN THE BED OF YASHODA. THEN BRING BACK THE GIRL THAT HAS BEEN BORN TO HER.

AND FORTHWITH VISHNU ASSUMED THE FORM OF A SMALL DARK BABY, WHO CAME TO BE KNOWN AS KRISHNA.

* A COWHERD CHIEF AT GOKUL

AS SOON AS VASUDEVA RETURNED WITH THE BABY GIRL, THE SLEEPING GUARDS WOKE UP.

A BABY'S CRY! THE EIGHTH CHILD OF DEVAKI IS BORN. KAMSA MUST BE TOLD.

WHEN KAMSA STOMPED IN —

DON'T KILL THIS BABY. IT'S ONLY A GIRL. LET ME KEEP HER, DEAR BROTHER.

IN REPLY, KAMSA MERELY SNATCHED THE INFANT FROM HER HAND...

...AND DASHED IT TO THE GROUND.

AND LO! TO HIS ALARM, THE BABY ROSE INTO THE SKY AND STOOD TRANSFORMED AS YOGAMAYA.

WHAT WOULD YOU GAIN BY KILLING ME, FOOLISH ONE? YOUR DESTROYER SURVIVES ELSEWHERE.

LATER, KAMSA SENT SEVERAL OF HIS ASURAS TO DESTROY THE INFANTS AT GOKUL WHOSE SENSATIONAL EXPLOITS * WORRIED HIM.

POOTANA, TRINAVARTA, AGHASURA, DHENUKA, PRALAMBA — ALL SLAIN BY THOSE TWO CHILDREN — KRISHNA AND BALARAMA!

* FOR DETAILS READ AMAR CHITRA KATHA NO. 501 — KRISHNA.

I SHALL HOLD A WRESTLING MATCH AT A BOW FESTIVAL, INVITE BOTH OF THEM TO MATHURA FOR IT AND FINISH THEM ONCE AND FOR ALL.

DELIGHTED BY THE INVITATION, THE BOYS CAME TO MATHURA. AS THEY PASSED THE HALL WHERE THE BOW WAS DISPLAYED—

AH! I MUST BEND IT.

KRISHNA NOT ONLY BENT THE BOW BUT PULLED ITS STRING SO TAUT THAT IT BROKE WITH A RESOUNDING CRASH...

...WHICH REACHED KAMSA'S EARS AS HE RELAXED IN HIS PALACE.

THE SNAP OF A BOW. DREAD FILLS MY BEING. CHANURA AND MUSHTIKA MUST NOT FAIL ME.

THE DAY OF THE FESTIVAL DAWNED. THE TRUMPET GAVE THE SIGNAL FOR THE GAMES TO BEGIN. THE MIGHTY WRESTLER CHANURA TOOK ON KRISHNA, AND HIS PARTNER, MUSHTIKA, BALARAMA.

EFFORTLESSLY THE BOYS FOUGHT AND DEFEATED THE CHAMPIONS.

KAMSA WAS FURIOUS. FEAR GRIPPED HIS HEART.

DRIVE THE BOYS OUT OF THE CITY. PUT THE TRAITOR VASUDEVA TO DEATH.

BEFORE THE ORDER COULD BE CARRIED OUT, KRISHNA LEAPT ONTO THE DAIS.

BHOOMI DEVI HAS BEEN RELIEVED OF THE HEAVIEST PART OF HER BURDEN.

IN THE YEARS THAT FOLLOWED, KRISHNA CAUSED THE DEATH OF KAMSA'S FATHER-IN-LAW, THE EVIL JARA-SANDHA...*

...AND KILLED HIS STAUNCH ALLY SHISHUPALA AND THEIR HORDES.

*SEE AMAR CHITRA KATHA NO. 518 — KRISHNA AND JARASANDHA

SOON AFTER THAT, KRISHNA'S COUSINS, THE VIRTUOUS PANDAVAS, WERE UNLAWFULLY DEPRIVED OF THEIR KINGDOM BY THEIR COUSINS, THE ARROGANT KAURAVAS, AND WAR BROKE OUT BETWEEN THEM.

I WILL SOON BE ABLE TO RID BHOOMI DEVI OF THE KAURAVAS.

IN THAT WAR THE KAURAVAS WERE EXTERMINATED.

NOW THERE REMAINS MY OWN RACE, THE VAIN YADAVAS WHO ARE PROSPEROUS AND INVINCIBLE BECAUSE OF MY UNCEASING GUIDANCE AND SUPPORT.

BACK AT DWARAKA—

I SHALL CAUSE THE ARROGANT YADAVA YOUTHS TO TEASE THE RISHIS AND INVITE THEIR OWN DESTRUCTION. THEN BALA-RAMA AND I WILL BE FREE TO WITHDRAW OUR-SELVES FROM THE WORLD.

AT THAT TIME, THE RISHIS—NARADA, VISHWAMITRA, KANVA, DURVASA, VASISHTHA AND OTHERS—WERE LIVING NEAR DWARAKA.

LET US DRESS SAMBA AS A PREGNANT GIRL AND REQUEST THE RISHIS TO PREDICT THE SEX OF THE EXPECTED CHILD.

AN EXCELLENT IDEA!

WHEN THEY PUT THEIR QUERY TO THE ALL-KNOWING RISHIS, HOWEVER—

HOW DARE THE PRANKSTERS TRIFLE WITH US?

SHE IS BEARING A MACE WHICH WILL DESTROY YOUR RACE, IGNORANT FOOLS!

THE TERRIFIED YOUTHS SEARCHED SAMBA.

WHAT SHALL WE DO WITH IT?

LET US TAKE IT TO UGRASENA AND CONFESS OUR CRIME.

WHEN UGRASENA HEARD THEIR STORY—

DON'T BE ALARMED. GRIND THE MACE INTO FINE POWDER AND SCATTER THE POWDER IN THE OCEAN.

THE ORDER WAS CARRIED OUT.

THIS PIECE IS TOO HARD. TRY AS I MIGHT I COULD NOT POUND IT.

THEN THROW IT IN AS IT IS.

BUT THE POWDER WAS WASHED BACK TO THE SHORE WHERE IT GREW INTO A GRASS CALLED ERAKA.

AND THE PIECE THAT COULD NOT BE GROUND WAS SWALLOWED BY A FISH.

THE FISH WAS CAUGHT BY THE HUNTER, JARA. WHEN HE CUT IT OPEN —

WHAT'S THIS? A PIECE OF IRON! IT WILL MAKE A FINE HEAD FOR ONE OF MY ARROWS.

MEANWHILE, SINCE THE YADU RACE WAS AS GOOD AS DESTROYED BY THE RISHI'S CURSE, BRAHMA, SHIVA, AND THE CELESTIALS CAME TO TAKE KRISHNA TO VAIKUNTHA. BUT —

I CANNOT LEAVE BEFORE THE YADU RACE IS DESTROYED, LEST IT OVERWHELM AND WIPE OUT THE WHOLE WORLD BEFORE IT IS ITSELF ANNIHILATED.

SOON AFTER, DWARAKA WAS PLAGUED BY FRIGHTENING OMENS. THE YADAVAS IN THEIR ALARM DRANK TOO MUCH LIQUOR, WERE INTOXICATED AND QUARRELLED AMONGST THEMSELVES.

ON THE SEVENTH DAY FROM NOW, DWARAKA WILL GO UNDER THE SEA. THE WORLD WILL BE INVADED BY THE SPIRIT OF KALI.

THE YADAVAS CONTINUED QUARRELLING. THEIR WEAPONS EXHAUSTED, THEY PULLED OUT HANDFULS OF THE DEADLY ERAKA GRASS.

LO! THE GRASS HAS TURNED INTO A MACE!

MY WORK IS DONE. THEY WILL SOON ANNIHILATE THEMSELVES.

HE WENT TO LOOK FOR BALARAMA AND FOUND HIM ALREADY SEATED IN MEDITATION BY THE SEASHORE.

HE HAS WITH-DRAWN HIMSELF FROM THE WORLD. I MUST FOLLOW HIM.

KRISHNA SAT UNDER A PEEPUL TREE AND LEANED BACK AGAINST IT.

JARA, THE HUNTER, WHO WAS PASSING BY, MISTOOK HIS FOOT TO BE THE MOUTH OF A DEER AND TOOK AIM.

THIS ARROW CANNOT FAIL ME. IT'S THE ONE I MADE WITH THE PIECE OF IRON THAT WAS STUCK IN THE FISH'S MAW.

THE ARROW FOUND ITS MARK AND BROUGHT TO AN END THE MOST GLORIOUS AVATAR OF LORD VISHNU.

THE HEAVENS RAINED FLOWERS AND CELESTIAL MUSIC FILLED THE SKY AS VISHNU PASSED ON FROM EARTH TO HIS ABODE IN VAIKUNTHA.

BUDDHA AVATAR

WITH KRISHNA'S DEPARTURE FROM EARTH, THE AGE OF KALI SET IN. HINDUISM LOST MUCH OF ITS PURITY. THE AUTHORITY OF THE VEDAS BECAME QUESTIONABLE. EMPTY RITUALS REPLACED TRUE DEVOTION TO GOD AND POWER-DRUNK BRAHMAN PRIESTS EXPLOITED AND OPPRESSED THE OTHER CASTES.

MAYADEVI, THE QUEEN OF THE SAKYA KING, SHUDDHODANA OF KAPILAVASTU, HAD A STRANGE DREAM. A WHITE ELEPHANT WITH SIX TUSKS PIERCED HER WOMB.

A FEW MONTHS LATER, SHE WAS PASSING THROUGH THE LUMBINI GARDENS ON HER WAY TO HER PARENTAL HOME. AS SHE RESTED BENEATH A SAL TREE, SHE GAVE BIRTH TO A CHILD.

IT'S A BOY, YOUR MAJESTY! HE IS AS LUSTROUS AS THE FULL MOON ABOVE.

LATER, AT THE PALACE, SAGE ASITA CAME TO SEE THE INFANT.

THIS CHILD WILL EITHER BECOME A GREAT EMPEROR OR WILL RENOUNCE THE WORLD AND BECOME A GREAT SAGE.

IF I CAN HELP IT, HE SHALL BECOME A KING OF KINGS AND **NOT** A SAGE.

WHEN SIDDHARTHA, AS THE CHILD WAS NAMED, GREW INTO A YOUNG LAD —

THE PRINCE SHALL NOT STEP BEYOND THE CONFINES OF HIS PALACE. LET HIM NEVER KNOW OF THE MISERIES OF OLD AGE, DISEASE OR DEATH. PROVIDE HIM WITH ALL THE LUXURIES IMAGINABLE.

AS SOON AS SIDDHARTHA, THE PRINCE WHO WAS IGNORANT OF THE PAIN AND MISERY OF THIS WORLD, CAME OF AGE, HE WAS MARRIED TO YASHODHARA, THE DAUGHTER OF A SAKYA NOBLE.

IN DUE COURSE, A SON WAS BORN TO THEM AND SIDDHARTHA HAD ALL THAT A MAN COULD WANT.

NOW SIDDHARTHA WILL NEVER THINK OF RENOUNCING THE WORLD.

BUT ONE DAY, A STRANGE URGE CAME OVER SIDDHARTHA. HE WENT TO SHUDDHODANA.

FATHER, I MUST GO OUT OF THE PALACE AND SEE MORE OF THE WORLD.

THEN I SHALL ORDER A SPECIAL CHARIOT FOR YOU. YOU MAY GO WHEN IT IS READY.

MEANWHILE, I SHALL SEE THAT THE ROUTE HE TAKES IS CLEAR OF ALL DISTURBING SIGHTS.

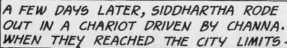

A FEW DAYS LATER, SIDDHARTHA RODE OUT IN A CHARIOT DRIVEN BY CHANNA. WHEN THEY REACHED THE CITY LIMITS —

DRIVE ON, CHANNA. I WISH TO GO BEYOND THE CITY.

AS THEY DROVE FURTHER —

CHANNA! HALT! WHY DOES THAT MAN BEND SO? WHY DOES HE USE A STICK?

IT IS OLD AGE, MY PRINCE—EVERYONE HAS TO GROW OLD.

EVEN I, CHANNA?

EVEN YOU, MY LORD.

WHEN THEY RETURNED TO THE PALACE, THE PRINCE BROODED OVER WHAT HE HAD SEEN.

I MUST SEE MORE, KNOW MORE. I MUST RIDE OUT AGAIN.

THIS TIME THEY SAW A SICK MAN, GROANING WITH PAIN.

WHAT'S WRONG WITH HIM, CHANNA?

HE IS ILL, MY LORD, WITH A PAINFUL DISEASE.

IS DISEASE PECULIAR TO HIM, CHANNA?

NO, MY LORD. EVEN YOU MAY FALL ILL.

SIDDHARTHA'S GREED FOR MORE KNOWLEDGE ON WHAT HAD HITHERTO BEEN CONCEALED FROM HIM GREW. HE MADE ANOTHER TOUR.

CHANNA! WHY ARE THEY CARRYING THAT MAN? IS HE OLD? IS HE ILL?

NO, MY LORD. IT'S MUCH WORSE. HE IS DEAD.

WILL I TOO HAVE TO DIE, CHANNA?

YES, MY LORD. ALL THAT IS BORN MUST DIE.

AS SIDDHARTHA PONDERED ON WHAT HE HAD SEEN, HIS LIFE OF EASE AND LUXURY BEGAN TO PALL ON HIM. HE NO LONGER FOUND JOY IN ANYTHING. HE WAS UNHAPPY AND DISTURBED.

MY SON CAN FALL ILL. YASHODHARA WILL GROW OLD AND UGLY. I WILL ULTIMATELY DIE. WHY WAS I BORN AT ALL?

AND HE RODE OUT ONCE AGAIN.

STOP, CHANNA! THAT FACE! HOW CALM! HOW SERENE IT LOOKS! WHO IS HE?

HE IS A MONK, MY LORD. HE HAS DEVOTED HIS LIFE TO THE PURSUIT OF TRUTH.

THAT NIGHT SIDDHARTHA MADE A DECISION.

I TOO SHALL DEVOTE MY LIFE TO THE PURSUIT OF TRUTH. I SHALL RENOUNCE MY ROYAL LIFE.

SO SIDDHARTHA LEFT THE PALACE AND BECAME AN ASCETIC. AFTER YEARS OF BITTER STRUGGLES, HE PERCEIVED TRUTH, AS HE SAT MEDITATING UNDER A BODHI TREE.

AND SIDDHARTHA, THE PRINCE, BECAME BUDDHA*— THE ENLIGHTENED ONE.

THEN BUDDHA CAME BACK TO LIVE AMONGST MEN AND TEACH THEM WHAT HE HAD LEARNT. HE HELD HIS FIRST SERMON IN THE DEER PARK AT SARNATH, NEAR VARANASI.

MAN SUFFERS BECAUSE HE IS BORN ON EARTH. HE IS BORN, DIES, AND IS BORN AGAIN BECAUSE OF HIS ATTACHMENTS, HIS DESIRES. DESIRE AND ATTACHMENT MUST BE DESTROYED. THEN MAN CEASES TO BE REBORN, CEASES TO SUFFER. DESIRE CAN BE DESTROYED.

FOR MANY YEARS DID BUDDHA PREACH, AND MANY WERE THOSE WHO SOUGHT REFUGE IN HIM AND IN HIS TEACHINGS. WHAT HE COULD GIVE, HOWEVER, TOUCHED BUT A DROP OF WATER IN THE SEA OF HUMANITY THAT WAS TOSSED BY THE MISERIES FORETOLD FOR THE KALI YUGA.

* SEE AMAR CHITRA KATHA NO. 510—BUDDHA.

KALKI AVATAR

MANY GOOD MEN WALKED THE EARTH AFTER BUDDHA BUT INSIGNIFICANT WAS THE EFFECT THEY HAD AGAINST THE GROWING SUPREMACY OF EVIL AND EVIL ONES ON EARTH. WITH THE ADVANCE OF SCIENTIFIC KNOWLEDGE THE LONGEVITY OF MAN HAS INCREASED BUT·WITH THE ADVANCE IN TECHNOLOGY, MAN'S LIFE HAS BECOME A NIGHTMARE OF HYPERTENSIONS AND POLLUTION. BUT NOT ALL HOPE IS LOST.

"FOR WHEN THE AGE REACHES ITS NADIR AND ITS WORST FORCES HAVE WELL NIGH SPENT THEMSHLVES, VISHNU WILL APPEAR AMONGST MORTALS IN HIS SATTVIC FORM AS KALKI.RIDING HIS CELESTIAL HORSE, HE WILL EXTERMINATE, BY THE MILLIONS, CORRUPT ROBBERS WHO BEAR HIGH POSITIONS IN LIFE AND WILL REINFORCE MORAL SENSE AND HUMANITARIAN VIEWS IN ALL GOOD PEOPLE, TILL TOWN AND COUNTRYSIDE WILL AGAIN ENJOY PEACE AND SECURITY. THEN WILL BEGIN A NEW CYCLE OF YUGAS WITH SATYA (TRUTH) AT ITS HEAD, WHOSE HUMAN GENERATIONS WILL BE IMBUED WITH GREAT MORAL, INTELLECTUAL,AND PHYSICAL STRENGTH, POSSESSING ALL IMMACULATE ATTRIBUTES."

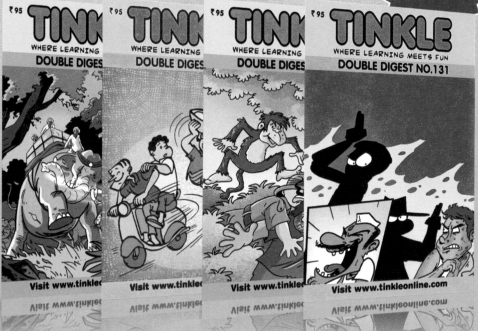